Good Girl, Sadie

Written by James L. Johnson

Dedicated to Michelle Johnson, my wonderful wife
and the best teacher I know.

Thank you for your support.

My name is Good Girl, Sadie Rose.

How do I know that? Because that is what my adoptive Mom and Dad have called me since we met one cold winter's night. I was just a puppy the first time they said

Good Girl, Sadie Rose.

Whenever I do something they like, they say my name. Like when I play fetch with my favorite toy, Orange Baby, a small squeaky pumpkin. Once I bring it back to them with my tail wagging, they say

good girl, Sadie Rose!

When my Dad and I play tugga-tugga with the rope and I growl and bark for him to play, he says

good girl, Sadie Rose!

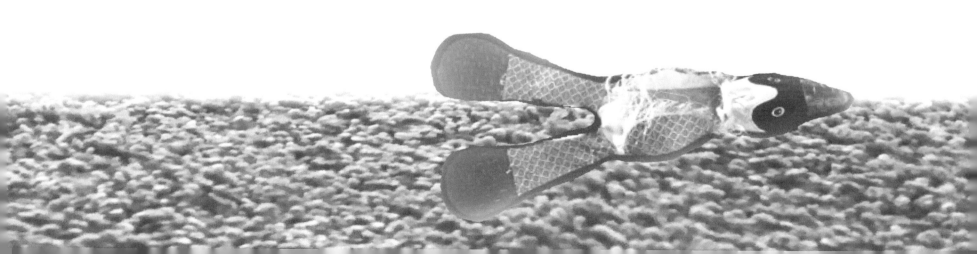

Pet

Rules

always

PLAY OFTEN

TAKE NAP

shake — lay down

AFFECTION

Then we play Sadie Pounce, my favorite game! Mom will toss Orange Baby behind the pillows on our couch. Then I fly up on to the couch and dive behind the pillow to get Orange Baby. When I bring it back to Mom, she says

Good Girl, Sadie Rose!

On our morning walks, I see lazy rabbits in our neighbors' yards. I bark and tell them to get to work. Then I walk over to them to make sure they can hear me, Mom and Dad say

good girl, Sadie Rose!

Mom and Dad think the squirrel in our backyard is friendly, he likes to run along our fence. He climbs in our trees and calls me into the yard every morning. I run out my doggie door and protect my Mom and Dad from him with barking and tail wagging. Mom and Dad always tell me

good girl, Sadie Rose!

I love bath time, especially once I am all clean. I make sure to shake and shake and shake. I know not to shake inside as it gets Mom and Dad wet, so when I need to, I shake outside after my bath, they say

good girl, Sadie Rose !

Mom and Dad like to groom me. I don't like it at all! But I am patient and allow them to do this. Afterward they give me treats and tell me how pretty I am. They say

good girl, Sadie Rose.

We have a lot of friends and family come to our home. I always let Mom and Dad know when someone is at the door by running and barking a welcome. Then I wag my tail and kiss the newcomers to let everyone know they are welcome to stay. They always say

Good Girl, Sadie Rose!

One day, my Mom got hurt. She hit her head, and I was the one to comfort her every day, all day while she healed. It was my job and I was very good at it. I sat with her right at her feet and would come snuggle close when she was asleep to make sure she was safe. She would always say

Good Girl, Sadie Rose.

When I was introduced to the new baby I was so excited.
I sniffed, licked and wagged my tail. A new baby boy.
Actually, Mom and Dad called him a grand baby. Whatever,
I still liked to give him kisses and be close to him. They
would tell me

Good girl, Sadie Rose....

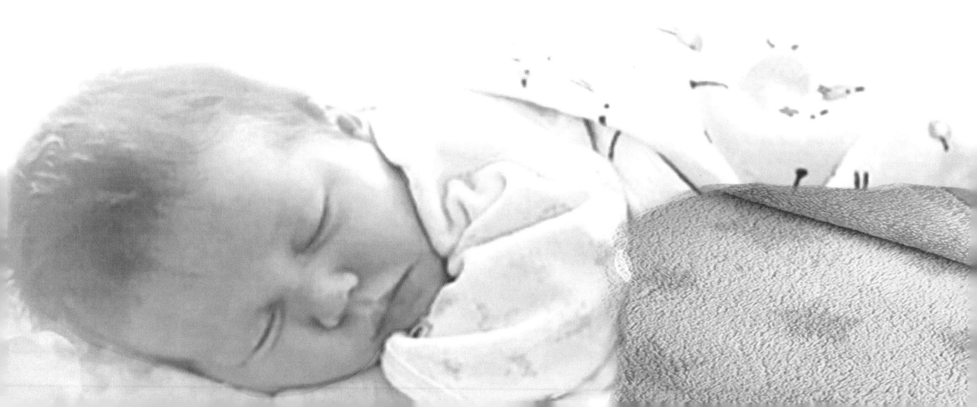

I love my home, and especially my Mom and Dad, who will forever call me

good girl, Sadie Rose..

Publisher's Cataloging-in-Publication data

Names: Johnson, James L., author. | Meyer, Tori, illustrator.
Title: Good girl, Sadie Rose / written by James L. Johnson ; [illustrations by Tori Meyer]
Description: Parker, CO: BookCrafters, 2021. | Summary: Sadie Rose is a very good dog.
Identifiers: ISBN: 978-1-7367537-0-5
Subjects: LCSH Dogs--Juvenile literature. | Family--Juvenile literature. | CYAC Dogs. | Family.
| BISAC PETS / Dogs / General
Classification: LCC SF426 .J64 2021 | DDC 636.7--dc23

CPSIA information can be obtained
at www.ICGtesting.com
Printed in the USA
LVRC012140200321
682007LV00014B/47

* 9 7 8 1 7 3 6 7 5 3 7 0 5 *